Limericks by Lear

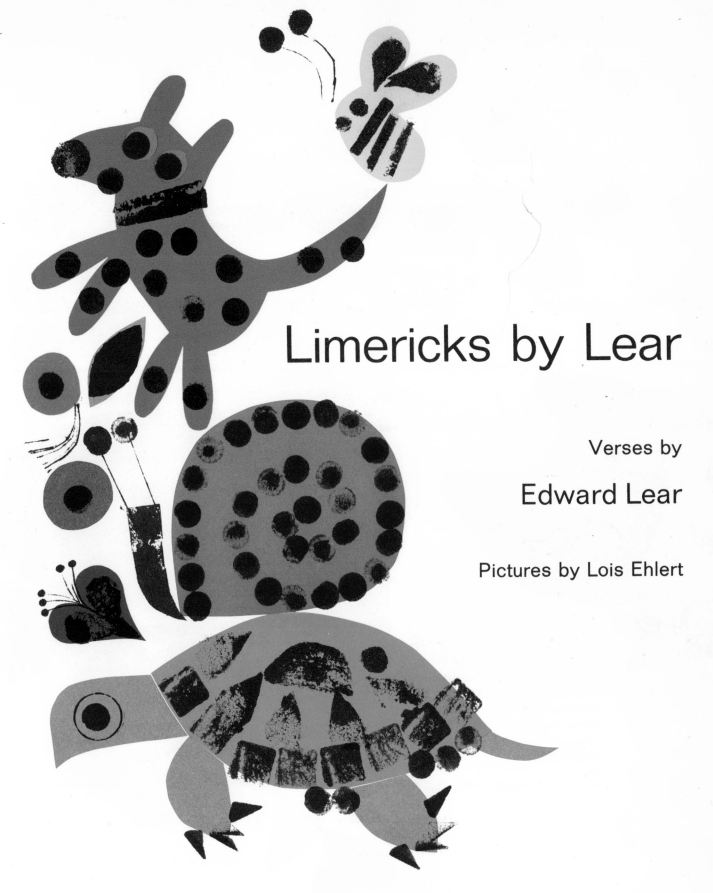

Limericks by Lear

Verses by

Edward Lear

Pictures by Lois Ehlert

The World Publishing Company / Cleveland and New York

Published by The World Publishing Company
2231 West 110th Street, Cleveland 2, Ohio
Published simultaneously in Canada by
Nelson, Foster & Scott Ltd.
Library of Congress Catalog Card Number: 65-22152
First Edition
E Z W P
Illustrations Copyright © 1965 by Lois Ehlert

Limericks by Lear

There was an Old Derry down Derry,
Who loved to see little folks merry;
So he made them a Book, and with laughter they shook
At the fun of that Derry down Derry.

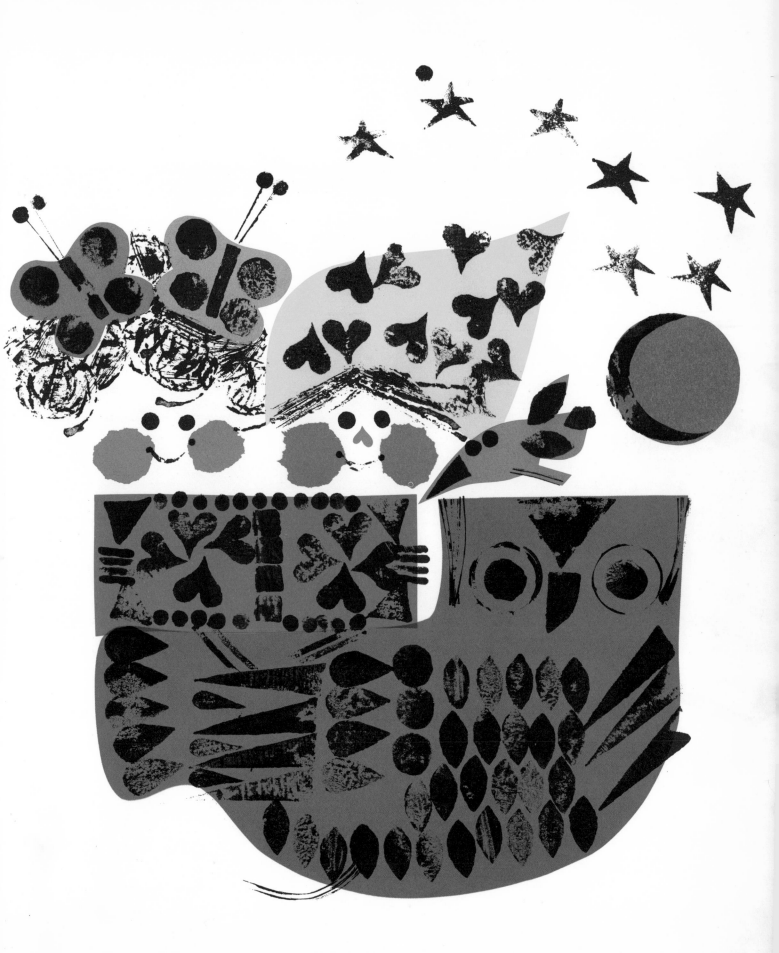

There was an old man of Dumbree,
Who taught little owls to drink tea;
For he said, "To eat mice, is not proper or nice,"
That amiable man of Dumbree.

There was a Young Lady of Bute,
Who played on a silver-gilt flute;
She played several jigs, to her uncle's white pigs,
That amusing Young Lady of Bute.

There was an Old Man with a beard,
Who said, "It is just as I feared!—
Two Owls and a Hen, four Larks and a Wren,
Have all built their nests in my beard!"

There was an old person of Ware,
Who rode on the back of a bear:
When they ask'd,—"Does it trot?"—he said "Certainly not!
He's a Moppsikon Floppsikon bear!"

There was an old person of Filey,
Of whom his acquaintance spoke highly;
He danced perfectly well, to the sound of a bell,
And delighted the people of Filey.

There was an old man of Boulak,
Who sate on a Crocodile's back;
But they said, "Tow'rds the night, he may probably bite,
Which might vex you. old man of Boulak!"

There was a Young Lady of Ryde,
Whose shoe-strings were seldom untied;
She purchased some clogs, and some small spotted dogs,
And frequently walked about Ryde.

There was an old person of Cannes,
Who purchased three fowls and a fan;
Those she placed on a stool, and to make them feel cool
She constantly fanned them at Cannes.

There was an old man of Blackheath,
Whose head was adorned with a wreath,
Of lobsters and spice, pickled onions and mice,
That uncommon old man of Blackheath.

There was an Old Man who said, "Hush!
I perceive a young bird in this bush!"
When they said—"Is it small?" He replied—"Not at all!
It is four times as big as the bush!"

There was a young lady in white,
Who looked out at the depths of the night;
But the birds of the air, filled her heart with despair,
And oppressed that young lady in white.

There was a Young Lady whose bonnet,
Came untied when the birds sat upon it;
But she said, "I don't care! all the birds in the air
Are welcome to sit on my bonnet!"

There was an old lady of France,
Who taught little ducklings to dance;
When she said, "Tick-a-tack!"—They only said, "Quack!"
Which grieved that old lady of France.

There was an old person of Bray,
Who sang through the whole of the day
To his ducks and his pigs, whom he fed upon figs,
That valuable person of Bray.

There was an old man in a tree,
Whose whiskers were lovely to see;
But the birds of the air, pluck'd them perfectly bare,
To make themselves nests in that tree.

There was an old man on the Border,
Who lived in the utmost disorder;
He danced with the cat, and made tea in his hat,
Which vexed all the folks on the Border.

There was an old man of Messina,
Whose daughter was named Opsibeena;
She wore a small wig, and rode out on a pig,
To the perfect delight of Messina.

There was an old person of Ealing,
Who was wholly devoid of good feeling;
He drove a small gig, with three Owls and a Pig,
Which distressed all the people of Ealing.

There was an old person of Ickley,
Who could not abide to ride quickly;
He rode to Karnak, on a tortoise's back,
That moony old person of Ickley.

There was a young person of Bantry,
Who frequently slept in the pantry;
When disturbed by the mice, She appeased them with rice,
That judicious young person of Bantry.